# Better Band Based Keys
## Rockschool

| | |
|---|---|
| Welcome To Debut Band Based Keys | 2 |
| Keyboard Notation Explained | 3 |
| Debut Band Based Keyboards Exams | 4 |

**Pieces:**

| | |
|---|---|
| **Bean Scent** | 5 |
| **Blockbuster** | 9 |
| **Detroit Spinna** | 13 |
| **Nick Of Time** | 17 |
| **Paisley On My Mind** | 21 |
| **Technotronica** | 25 |

| | |
|---|---|
| Technical Exercises | 28 |
| Sight Reading | 29 |
| Ear Tests | 31 |
| General Musicianship Questions | 32 |
| Entering Rockschool Exams | 33 |

# Welcome To Debut Band Based Keyboards

Welcome to the Rockschool Debut Band Based Keyboards pack. The book and CD contain everything needed to play BBK in this grade. The accompanying CD has full stereo mixes of each tune, backing tracks to play along with for practise and spoken two bar count-ins to each piece. Each piece is preceded by a Factfile containing information about the styles of music and suggested further listening. Playing tips can be found in the Walkthrough that follows each piece. If you have any queries about this or any other Rockschool exam, please call us on **0845 460 4747**, email us at *info@rockschool.co.uk* or visit our website *www.rockschool.co.uk*. Good luck!

### Entry Level Techniques In Debut

The nine Rockschool grades are divided into four levels. These levels correspond to the levels of the National Qualifications Framework (NQF). Details of all Rockschool's accredited qualifications can be found at *www.accreditedqualifications.org.uk*.

Debut Band Based Keyboards is part of the Entry Level. Entry Level is for players who are beginners and are looking to establish a simple and reliable technical facility. This will be shown through simple hand coordination in the delivery of very simple rhythms. Focus will be on maintaining solid pulse and understanding of combinations of note values and pitches.

**Debut**: Pieces will be no longer than one minute to enable the player to sustain concentration and fluency. They will use simple note values and rhythms. Hand coordination will be basic and phrases will generally fall within five finger shapes occasionally requiring some finger changes. Articulation will be limited to understanding values and pieces will be written for one instrument patch only. Any simple instrumental techniques will be written out the music.

### Types of keyboard

In order to play the pieces in this grade, you will need a keyboard with 61 keys with the following patches: acoustic piano, electric piano, organ, strings and synth.

# Keyboard Notation Explained

**THE MUSICAL STAVE** shows pitches and rhythms and is divided by lines into bars. Pitches are named after the first seven letters of the alphabet.

**THE TIME SIGNATURE** tells how many beats in a bar (top number), and the value of those beats (bottom number)

**Grace Note:** Play the grace note on or before the beat depending on the style of music, then move quickly to the note it leads onto.

**Spread Chord:** Play the chord from the bottom note to the top note, or the top note to the bottom note, as indicated by the arrow.

**Tremolando:** Oscillate at speed between marked notes.

**Pedal Marking:** Depress and then release the sustain pedal.

**Glissando:** Slide up (or down) the keyboard before playing note indicated.

**Finger Markings:** These numbers represent your fingers. 1 is the thumb, 2 the index finger and so on.

 (accent)   •  Accentuate note (play it louder).

 (accent)   •  Accentuate note with great intensity.

 (staccato)   •  Shorten time value of note.

 (tenuto)   •  Play for full value but separate from next note.

*D.%. al Coda*   •  Go back to the sign (%), then play until the bar marked *To Coda* ✛ then skip to the section marked ✛ *Coda*.

*D.C. al Fine*   •  Go back to the beginning of the song and play until the bar marked *Fine* (end).

   •  Repeat bars between signs.

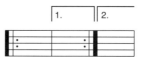   •  When a repeated section has different endings, play the first ending only the first time and the second ending only the second time.

# Band Based Keyboards Exams At Debut

There are **two** types of exam that can be taken using this pack: a Grade Exam and a Performance Certificate.

**Debut Band Based Keyboards Exam: this is for players who want to develop performance and technical skills**

Players wishing to enter for a Debut Band Based Keyboards exam need to prepare **three** pieces of which **one** may be a free choice piece chosen from outside the printed repertoire. In addition you must prepare the technical exercises in the book, undertake a sight reading test, take an ear test and answer general musicianship questions. Samples of these tests are printed in the book along with audio examples on the CD.

**Debut Band Based Keyboards Performance Certificate: this is for players who want to perform in a range of styles**

To enter for your Debut Band Based Keyboards Performance Certificate you play pieces only. You can choose any **five** of the six tunes printed in this book, or you can choose to bring in up to **two** free choice pieces as long as they meet the standards set out by Rockschool. Free choice piece checklists can be found at *www.rockschool.co.uk*.

### Debut Band Based Keyboards Marking Schemes

The table below shows the marking scheme for the Debut Band Based Keyboards exam. **Please note that all accredited Entry Level qualifications are certificated at 'pass' only, regardless of the mark achieved above 65%.**

| ELEMENT | PASS |
|---|---|
| Piece 1 | 13 out of 20 |
| Piece 2 | 13 out of 20 |
| Piece 3 | 13 out of 20 |
| Technical Exercises | 11 out of 15 |
| Sight Reading | 6 out of 10 |
| Ear Tests | 6 out of 10 |
| General Musicianship Questions | 3 out of 5 |
| **Total Marks** | **Pass: 65%+** |

The table below shows the marking scheme for the Debut Band Based Keyboards Performance Certificate. **Please note that all accredited Entry Level qualifications are certificated at 'pass' only, regardless of the mark achieved above 70%.**

| ELEMENT | PASS |
|---|---|
| Piece 1 | 14 out of 20 |
| Piece 2 | 14 out of 20 |
| Piece 3 | 14 out of 20 |
| Piece 4 | 14 out of 20 |
| Piece 5 | 14 out of 20 |
| **Total Marks** | **Pass: 70%+** |

SONG TITLE: BEAN SCENT
GENRE: ACID JAZZ
TEMPO: 95 BPM
KEY: A MINOR
PATCHES: ELECTRIC PIANO

FEATURES: COUNTER-MELODY

COMPOSER: HUSSEIN BOON
ARRANGER: JEREMY WARD

PERSONNEL: DEIDRE CARTWRIGHT (GTR)
HENRY THOMAS (BASS)
GEORGE GAVIN (DRUMS)
ALASTAIR GAVIN (KEYS)

## BACKGROUND INFO

Acid Jazz was a style that enjoyed a certain popularity at the beginning of the 1990s in the UK. The style was a fusion of hip hop, jazz and funk with overtones of electronic dance music. Key artists from the time were Freak Power, Brand New Heavies, Incognito and early Jamiroquai.

## THE BIGGER PICTURE

The origins of Acid Jazz lie in jazz-funk popularised by American musicians such as Herbie Hancock and Roy Ayers and in electronic dance music. The music could be played equally either by using samples triggered by a DJ or as a group of live musicians using 'jazz' chords and chord progressions.

## NOTES

The keyboard parts of the early Acid Jazz records recalled the Fender Rhodes sound of many soul and funk records of the late 60s and early 70s, giving washes of melodic colour. A good example of this is Jamiroquai's 'Blow Your Mind', in which the Rhodes sound creates variety in what is otherwise a very repetitive groove.

## RECOMMENDED LISTENING

Freak Power's 'Turn On, Tune In, Cop Out' (1993) was made famous through its association with a Levi Jeans ad. Brand New Heavies' *Brother Sister* (1990) features the hits 'Midnight at the Oasis' and 'Dream on Dreamer', while the first Jamiroquai record *Emergency on Planet Earth* (1993) contains the title track and 'When You Gonna Learn', originally released on the Acid Jazz label before the band signed to Sony.

# Bean Scent

Debut Band Based Keyboards

# Walkthrough

This jazz style piece needs a cool sound so choose a patch that is warm. A suggestion is Suitcase or Fender Rhodes. The tempo is not very fast and there might be a temptation to rush the quarter notes so spend some time listening to the backing track and clapping/tapping the beat.

**Bars 1–8:**

In bars 1–4 the right hand is playing a counter-melody (a melody that works with the main one on the backing track) that is repeated in bars 5–8. It needs to be given smoothly (legato) and with an even sound. Fingering is important here so start with your 5th finger. To fully achieve an even sound keep your fingers very close to the keys. This way you will be able to judge the pressure you play with. The further away from the key you play the notes the more unreliable the sound will be. Be careful that you count steadily as you have three different values in the first two bars: dotted half, half and quarter notes. The left hand chords need to be balanced and steady. Between the two hands there should be a clear sense of 4 beats in every bar. If you are correct with the fingers in the left hand you will not have to move throughout the piece so make sure that the first notes are played with fingers 1 & 5.

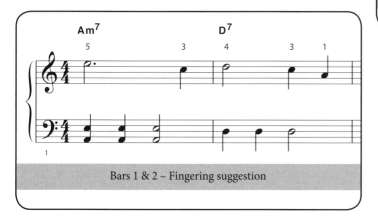

Bars 1 & 2 – Fingering suggestion

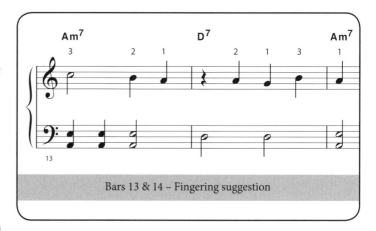

Bars 13 & 14 – Fingering suggestion

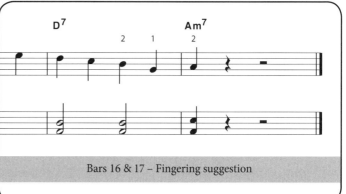

Bars 16 & 17 – Fingering suggestion

**Bars 9–16:**

You will need to make sure that in bar 10 you observe the quarter note rest. This might feel a little strange at first as in the previous eight bars the quarter note rest is in a different place. In bar 14 you will need to change fingers in the right hand to finger 2 and then back to finger 1 on the first beat of bar 15. You will also have to stretch fingers 2 & 1 on beats 3 & 4 in bar 16. Make sure that you only play a quarter note in the last bar.

SONG TITLE: BLOCKBUSTER

GENRE: ROCK

TEMPO: 80 BPM

KEY: E MINOR

PATCHES: ORGAN

FEATURES: POWER CHORDS

COMPOSER: HUSSEIN BOON

ARRANGER: JEREMY WARD

PERSONNEL: DEIDRE CARTWRIGHT (GTR)

HENRY THOMAS (BASS)

GEORGE GAVIN (DRUMS)

ALASTAIR GAVIN (KEYS)

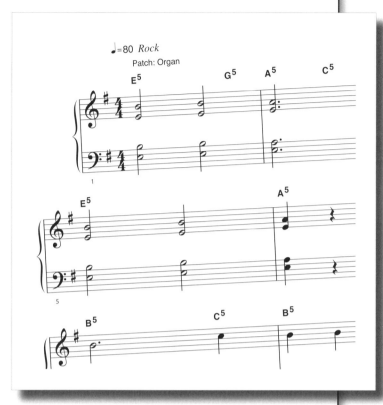

## BACKGROUND INFO

The Midlands has produced any number of hard rock bands. The most famous of these are Black Sabbath and Judas Priest. Between them they released a series of classic albums that helped define heavy metal.

## THE BIGGER PICTURE

Judas Priest and Black Sabbath rode the wave of British bands in America at a time when Led Zeppelin were stadium gods and the nearest home grown acts of any importance were Aerosmith and Kiss. This success paved the way for the 'second wave' of rock acts that followed, such as Def Leppard. There was a bizarre price to be paid, however. In the 1990s Judas Priest were caught up in the first of a number of 'subliminal message' law suits, part of the conservative backlash against heavy metal music. The songwriters were found not guilty.

## NOTES

Judas Priest was one of the first bands to pioneer the use of duelling guitarists in heavy rock: K K Downing and Glen Tipton. Tipton came to the guitar relatively late in his life but had been playing the piano since he was a boy. Tipton incorporated keyboards into several Judas Priest tracks, including 'Epitaph', a piano song from the classic Priest album *Sad Wings of Destiny* (1976). Later keyboard contributions were made by sessioneer and Deep Purple stalwart Don Airey on *Painkiller* (1990), *Demolition* (2001), *Angel of Retribution* (2005) and *Nostradamus* (2006).

## RECOMMENDED LISTENING

Judas Priest's classic 70s and early 80s albums set the standard for metallers to follow. Notable amongst these is *British Steel* (1980) which features the marvellous 'Breaking the Law' amongst others. This record, released immediately after the live set *Unleashed in the East* (1979), propelled the band to superstardom, particularly in America.

# Blockbuster

**Hussein Boon**

# Walkthrough

This is a heavy rock track and so you will need to pick an organ patch that can balance with distorted guitars. Most keyboards have a rock organ patch. More importantly you will also need to work out which octave you need to play to ensure the sound is at the written pitch. Most keyboards automatically sound an octave lower than the note you play with organ patches, but you need to make sure. An easy way of doing this is to play middle C with the acoustic piano voice and then middle C with your chosen organ voice. It will be clear if the sound is lower. If it is you will have to play the piece an octave higher than written. This can seem a little disorientating at first but you will soon get used to it.

### Bars 1–4:

The opening bar must be well coordinated and you will need to make sure both hands play at the same time. You will also need to ensure that they hold for the same length. Take a few moments notice that the lower note in each had remains the same and it is the upper note that changes. When playing an organ sound you will need to play the full note values to make sure the sound is not too disjointed. In bar 2 make sure that you count the dotted half note fully to avoid coming off it too quickly and playing beat 4 too early.

In bar 3 you will need to have a 'seesaw' feel between the hands but make sure that you do not release one hand before you have played the other. If you do there will gaps in the sound. You should be able o hear a clearly connected 4 beats. In bar 4 the hands are playing in unison (the same notes in each hand) and try to ensure that you keep each note pressed down until you have sounded the following note. This is called overlapping and is a technique organists use to ensure that the sound produced is smooth.

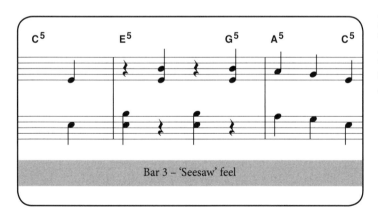
Bar 3 – 'Seesaw' feel

### Bars 5–10:

Bar 5 is the same as bar 1 but note that in bar 6 you only play a quarter note: use the rest to move your hand position up a note. In bar 10 you will need to do a quick finger change so spend some time securing this. In this bar you will hold onto the first note whilst you walk down in each hand. This is a very stylistic effect for organ.

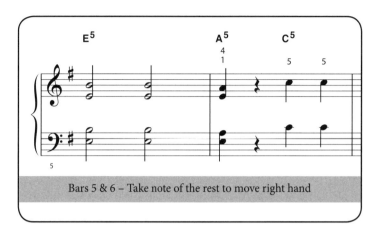
Bars 5 & 6 – Take note of the rest to move right hand

### Bars 11–16:

In bar 11 the chords are parallel in both hands. This means that you simply move your hand position down one note. Make sure you show the quarter note rest in bar 12 so that you can move your hand position back up one note. Bars 13 & 14 are similar but use the 'seesaw' idea. In bars 15–16 the downward chords continue and be careful that you move your hands down in the same shape but watch beat 4 of bar 16 is only the lower note.

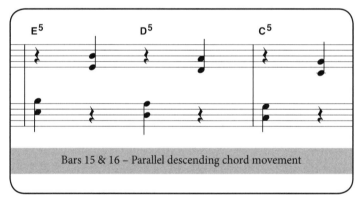
Bars 15 & 16 – Parallel descending chord movement

### Bars 17–19:

This is another place where the stylistic held note is used. Make sure you start with finger 1 (thumb) in the right hand and the 5th finger in the left hand. Try to make this passage very bold and smooth.

# Detroit Spinna

SONG TITLE: DETROIT SPINNA
GENRE: TECHNO/ELECTRO
TEMPO: 120 BPM
KEY: A MINOR
PATCHES: SYNTH

FEATURES: SILENT FINGER CHANGE

COMPOSER: ADRIAN YORK
ARRANGER: JEREMY WARD

PERSONNEL: DEIDRE CARTWRIGHT (GTR)
HENRY THOMAS (BASS)
GEORGE GAVIN (DRUMS)
ALASTAIR GAVIN (KEYS)

## BACKGROUND INFO

Techno is a form of electronic dance music that emerged in the 1980s after the demise of disco. There are many variants of the genre but most are agreed that the style originated in Detroit, Michigan. The style is generally instrumental and was designed mainly for playing out by DJs.

## THE BIGGER PICTURE

Techno fused together the electronic disco beats of European synth-pop producers such as Giorgio Moroder ('Love to Love You Baby', 'I Feel Love') with the African American styles such as Chicago House, funk and jazz. The main originators were three high school buddies: Juan Atkins, Derrick May and Kevin Saunderson, the so-called 'Belleville Three'. They wrote and collaborated on a large number of records under a wealth of different monikers and guises. The sound quickly proved very influential in the pop charts: the looping bass and drum patterns can be found all over Stock, Aiken and Waterman records such as those released by Kylie Minogue and Rick Astley in the late 1980s.

## NOTES

The development of digital synthesis gave producers with access to software and a sample bank almost complete freedom to experiment and create music without the need for 'traditional' music skills. The commercial possibilities could also be exploited more adeptly as what mattered to listeners was the quality of the music rather than who was playing it.

## RECOMMENDED LISTENING

Derrick May's dancefloor anthem from the late 1980s 'Strings of Life', recorded under the pseudonym Rhythim is Rhythim (sic) can be found in several remix compilations. Kevin Saunderson's most evidently commercial records 'Paradise', 'Good Life' and particularly 'Big Fun' can be found on *Inner City Paradise* (1989) a collaboration with singer Paris Grey.

# Detroit Spinna

**Adrian York**

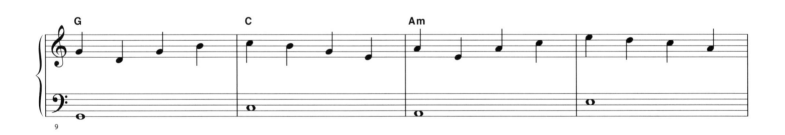

# Walkthrough

You will need a bright sounding synth patch for this piece as the style is techno and so has a lot of electronic sounds in it. Choose one that has a good attack (a sound that responds quickly to your fingers). A suggestion is Fargo. You will also need to work out which octave you need to play to ensure the sound is at the written pitch. Most keyboards automatically sound an octave lower than the note you play with synth patches, but you need to make sure. An easy way of doing this is to play middle C with the acoustic piano voice and then middle C with your chosen synth voice. It will be clear if the sound is lower. If it is you will have to play the piece an octave higher than written. This can seem a little disorientating at first but you will soon get used to it.

This piece looks quite simple but there are some finger changes and small hand position changes that will require patience and slow practise.

**Bars 1–4:**
The first thing you need to establish is the distance between the hands. The opening is two octaves apart (between right and left hands). The right hand should begin with finger 3 to allow you to negotiate bar 3. Make sure that the quarter notes are smooth (legato) and that you do not rush them. The left hand has quarter notes throughout and uses the upper note as an anchor.

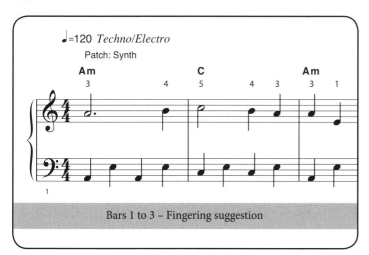

Bars 1 to 3 – Fingering suggestion

**Bars 5–7:**
Make sure that you notice the change in the upper note of the left hand here until bar 7. You will have to move your thumb up. In bar 7 the right hand will have to cross finger 2 over the thumb to cover the E. Try to then silently slide the thumb onto this note during the 4 beats without it sounding again. This is a very useful technique to develop.

**Bars 8–12:**
This is the melody part of the piece and it needs to be delivered smoothly and evenly. Fingering is very important and there are quite a few stretches needed. From bar 9 the

intervals (distance between the notes) is quite large and some slow practise will be needed to be able to control each quarter note to sound balanced. There is considerable use of fingers 4 & 5 which tend to be the weaker ones so more practise might be needed here. You will need to make sure that the long left hand notes are fully achieved to help the harmony line.

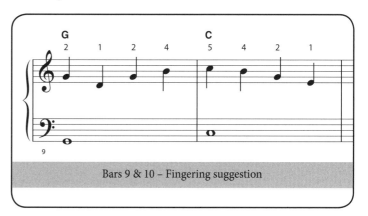

Bars 9 & 10 – Fingering suggestion

**Bars 13–16:**
You will need to ensure that the right hand begins bar 13 using the thumb and that in bar 15 you change finger 3 silently to the thumb to be able achieve the notes in the final bar. The left hand is a repeat of bars 5–7 and remember to note the change in the upper note in bar 15.

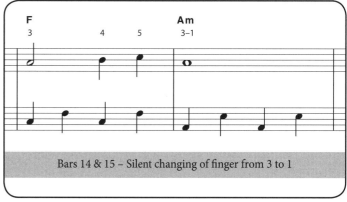

Bars 14 & 15 – Silent changing of finger from 3 to 1

SONG TITLE:  IN THE NICK OF TIME
GENRE:  GUITAR POP
TEMPO:  90 BPM
KEY:  E MINOR
PATCHES:  ORGAN

FEATURES:  CO-ORDINATED TWO NOTE CHORDS

COMPOSER:  JASON WOOLLEY
ARRANGER:  JEREMY WARD

PERSONNEL:  DEIDRE CARTWRIGHT (GTR)
HENRY THOMAS (BASS)
GEORGE GAVIN (DRUMS)
ALASTAIR GAVIN (KEYS)

## BACKGROUND INFO

Britpop produced many legends but nothing else could quite match Jarvis Cocker and Pulp. Pulp produced a string of effortless hits from the mid 1990s and was a cool antidote to the swagger of Oasis and the art school cleverness of Blur.

## THE BIGGER PICTURE

The history of 'Britpop' is by now generally well-known. The scene was dominated by a north-south divide between Oasis and Blur that diverted a lot of attention away from the quality of the music. Pulp's members, who mostly came from Sheffield, were rather older than their counterparts, in a band that was first formed in 1978. Jarvis Cocker's wry take on the human condition in songs such as 'Common People' stands in contrast to the 'cockernee' chirpiness of 'Parklife' or the overblown cacophony that is 'D'You Know What I Mean?'

## NOTES

Pulp combined a driving guitar-based edginess with often lush keyboard parts played by the band's keyboard player Candida Doyle. Belfast-born Candida joined in 1984 along with her brother Magnus. Doyle appeared on Pulp's second major record, *Freaks* (1987) and on all other major releases after that. Her keyboard style and sound palette are varied and it is an integral part of the Pulp production.

## RECOMMENDED LISTENING

1995's *Different Class* is essential listening having, as it does, both 'Common People', and 'Disco 2000' but the rest of the songs are universally good. It was preceded by their major label debut *His 'n' Hers* (1994).

# In The Nick Of Time

Jason Woolley

# Walkthrough

The organ sound for this piece needs to cut through the backing and so you need quite a bright sounding patch. Don't choose anything too heavy like a rock organ. You also need to work out which octave you need to play to ensure the sound is at the written pitch. Most keyboards automatically sound an octave lower than the note you play with organ patches, but you need to make sure. An easy way of doing this is to play middle C with the acoustic piano voice and then middle C with your chosen organ voice. It will be clear if the sound is lower. If it is you will have to play the piece an octave higher than written. This can seem a little disorientating at first but you will soon get used to it.

### Bars 1–2:
The most important thing is that you begin with the correct finger in each hand. The right hand requires finger 2 and the left hand finger 4. Bars 1–2 have both hands moving in similar motion (the same way) and using the same values (half notes). This will require that you are well coordinated and that both hands hold the notes for the same length. A useful organ technique to develop is to learn to keep the note sounding and held down until you have fully played the next note. This is called overlapping and means that the sound is smooth and connected (legato). Make sure that you take the left hand off to allow the right hand to sound separately in bar 2. These quarter notes can be slightly separated but not too staccato.

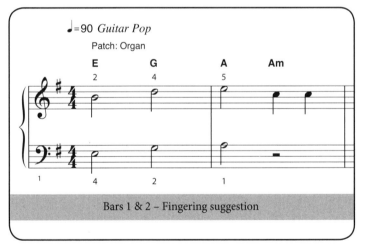

Bars 1 & 2 – Fingering suggestion

### Bars 3–4:
Bar 3 is similar in idea to bar 1, using the same notes, but you will need a 'seesaw' motion between the hands. Remember, do not release one note until you have fully played the next. Bar 4 has the right hand playing 8th notes instead of quarter notes and you need to ensure that these are not rushed and are played smoothly.

### Bars 5–8:
These bars are similar to the opening but be careful that you notice that in bar 6 the 8th notes use three pitches and not two (as in bar 4). Also notice that the left hand has two

quarter notes on beats 3 & 4 in bar 8. There might be a temptation to rush these so make sure there is a steady count of 4 in this bar.

### Bars 9–12:
These chords need a different approach and need to sound quite staccato. Make sure that both hands are balanced and that the gap is the same in both hands. Also ensure that the half note in bar 10 is fully realised as it acts as a little rest point. In bar 12 you will need to make the one hand position change of the whole piece in the right hand. You will need to move finger 5 up to and F♯. As it is the smallest finger and the black note is situated further up the keyboard you will need to bear this in mind and play the previous notes deeper into the keyboard. There can be a slight gap between the F♯ and the C to allow you to reposition.

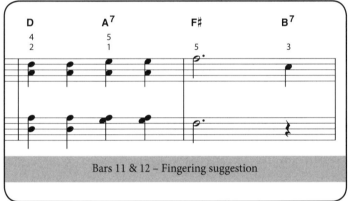

Bars 11 & 12 – Fingering suggestion

### Bars 13–16:
The last four bars use material that has been used in other parts of the song. Just ensure that the hands are coordinated in the last bar and that the half note is given full value.

SONG TITLE: PAISLEY ON MY MIND
GENRE: COUNTRY
TEMPO: 100 BPM
KEY: G MAJOR
PATCHES: PIANO

FEATURES: ROCKING COUNTRY LH

COMPOSER: JOE BENNETT
ARRANGER: JEREMY WARD

PERSONNEL: DEIDRE CARTWRIGHT (GTR)
HENRY THOMAS (BASS)
GEORGE GAVIN (DRUMS)
ALASTAIR GAVIN (KEYS)

## BACKGROUND INFO

This track celebrates the country and western music style which has had a tremendous impact on the development of popular music since 1945.

## THE BIGGER PICTURE

The term 'country music' covers a whole range of styles commonly found in the southern United States and the Appalachian mountains of West Virginia. It includes almost everything from singing cowboys and bluegrass to the modern commercial phenomenon of Garth Brooks. It is essentially a 'white' musical genre but it is tied in to many black music forms: the welding of country music to rhythm and blues, for example, lead to the first rock 'n' roll records and to the rise of Elvis Presley.

## NOTES

The piano has always featured prominently on country records and one of its greatest exponents was Floyd Cramer. Cramer is principally known as one of the popularisers of the so-called 'Nashville Sound' and he was an exponent of an effortlessly sounding piano style called 'slip-note'. Cramer was much in demand in Nashville as a session player and made innumerable recordings. He also toured extensively with the guitarist Chet Atkins who had been Elvis' first recording engineer. Cramer, who died in 1997, had a career which crossed over from country to pop and he covered many soul and blues hits.

## RECOMMENDED LISTENING

Compilations of Cramer's recordings can be found almost everywhere: twenty of the best, including his biggest hit 'Last Date' (1960), can be found on *The Essential Floyd Cramer* (1994). It is his signature piano playing that graces Elvis' first hit 'Heartbreak Hotel' and he also played on early Roy Orbison and Everly Brothers records.

# Paisley On My Mind

### Joe Bennett

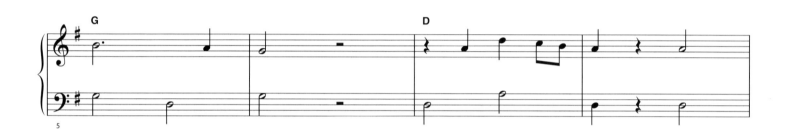

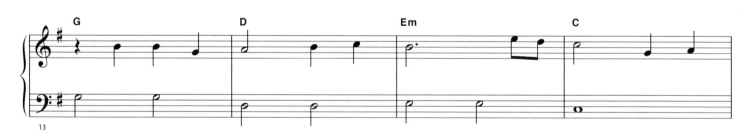

Debut Band Based Keyboards

# Walkthrough

This country track looks quite straightforward but there are a few areas that will need care and some slow practise. One of the possible areas is the tempo. It is quite slow and as much of the writing is in quarter notes there might be a temptation to rush at times. Take the time to listen to the backing track and tapping along to ensure you understand the relaxed nature of the piece. There are a few finger and hand position changes needed to ensure a fluent delivery.

### Bars 1–4:

The first thing you must be aware of is the three note lead in from the guitar. Use these three beats to be in position and to make sure you have the correct pace. The right hand should begin with finger 3 and the left hand with finger 1 (thumb). You must make sure that the half notes are given their correct value and that the hands are well coordinated. Country music needs to sound clean and neatly articulated. You will notice that the left hand is alternating (rocking) between the same two notes but make sure you observe the rest in bar 2. The right hand has a quarter note rest in bar 3 that adds a rhythmic touch so make sure it's clear.

### Bars 5–8:

Bar 5 has the first area that will need attention. In the left hand the rocking that has gone on in the previous bars is interrupted by a repetition of the G. This might catch you unawares so be careful. Also watch that the half note rest in bar 6 is used. You will need to change hand position in the left hand and put finger 5 on the D. This is only temporary for bars 5 & 6 and you should use the quarter note rest in bar 8 to return to the original position. In the right hand these are first 8th notes in bar 7 and you need to make sure these are not rushed. You will also need the rest in bar 7 to change to finger 1 on the A.

Bars 5 to 7 – Fingering suggestion

### Bars 9–12:

These four bars are relatively straight forward as long you are correct in fingering. In bar 12 you will have to cross finger 2 over in the left hand to be able to reach the A. Use the half note rest in bar 12 to reposition the right hand to the original position.

### Bars 13–20:

In bars 14–15 you will need to use finger 4 on beat 4 and finger 2 on beat 1 in the right hand to enable you to be in position for the 8th notes at the end of the bar. Make sure the left hand note in bar 16 is given its full value. In bar 17 the right hand has three repeated Bs that need to be given as much value each as possible. Try to avoid these sounding staccato as this would be out of character with the rest of the piece. The values in bar 19 are quite long and the dotted half note will need careful counting to avoid moving too early onto beat 4.

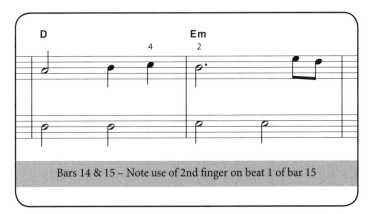

Bars 14 & 15 – Note use of 2nd finger on beat 1 of bar 15

SONG TITLE: TECHNOTRONICA
GENRE: TECHNO/ELECTRO
TEMPO: 70 BPM
KEY: E MINOR
PATCHES: STRINGS

FEATURES: RH FINGER CROSSING

COMPOSER: JOHN EACOTT
ARRANGER: JEREMY WARD

PERSONNEL: DEIDRE CARTWRIGHT (GTR)
HENRY THOMAS (BASS)
GEORGE GAVIN (DRUMS)
ALASTAIR GAVIN (KEYS)

## BACKGROUND INFO

Techno is a form of electronic dance music that emerged in the 1980s after the demise of disco. There are many variants of the genre but most are agreed that the style originated in Detroit, Michigan. The style is generally instrumental and is designed mainly for playing out by DJs.

## THE BIGGER PICTURE

Techno fused together the electronic disco beats of European synth-pop producers such as Giorgio Moroder ('Love to Love You Baby', 'I Feel Love') with the African American styles such as Chicago House, funk and jazz. The main originators were three high school buddies: Juan Atkins, Derrick May and Kevin Saunderson, the so-called 'Belleville Three'. They wrote and collaborated on a large number of records under a wealth of different monikers and guises. Since that time, techno has splintered into a number of sub-branches, including minimal, hardcore, ambient and intelligent dance music, personified by artists such as Richard James, better known as Aphex Twin.

## NOTES

The development of digital synthesis gave producers with access to software and a sample bank almost complete freedom to experiment and create music without the need for 'traditional' music skills. The commercial possibilities could also be exploited more adeptly as what mattered to listeners was the quality of the music rather than who was playing it.

## RECOMMENDED LISTENING

Juan Atkins, considered by many to be the Godfather of the techno style, working under the name Model 500, released the highly eclectic *Mind and Body* in 1989. Aphex Twin's first two commercial albums, *Selected Ambient Works 85-92* and *Volume II* were released in 1992 and 1994 respectively.

# Technotronica

**John Eacott**

# Walkthrough

This Techno track requires a string sound that will articulate the line clearly. You do not want a patch that has too little attack (takes time to sound after you have pressed the key). Go for a synth string sound or orchestral strings. There is a lot of interplay between the hands in this piece and the hands will need to be balanced. The effect should be as if two sets of strings (cellos and violins) are having a dialogue.

**Bars 1–4:**
Bar 1 requires you set up a 'seesaw' motion between the hands to ensure that there is a clear and steady four beats heard. Take time to listen to the backing track as the tempo is quite slow and there might be a temptation to rush some of the quarter notes. To develop a string technique try to hold down one note until the next note has sounded. This way you achieve a connected line. This is called overlapping and is a useful technique to have. Watch that the 8th notes in bar 4 are not given too early or are uneven. These are a lead in to the next phrase and should connect smoothly to it.

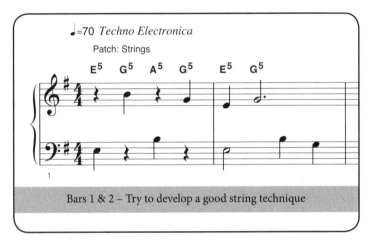

Bars 1 & 2 – Try to develop a good string technique

**Bars 5–12:**
Much of these four bars are similar with the addition of the first note in the right hand in bar 5. This is there to connect the 8th notes from the previous bar. In bar 8 you will notice that the 8th notes descend. This is in preparation for the following phrase which will need some finger attention.

**Bars 9–12:**
The right hand will have finger 3 on the first beat and so you will need to cross the third finger over on beat 4 to enable you to play the next two beats in bar 10. Watch that the left hand long notes are achieved here to help support the harmony. Use the quarter note rest in bar 10 to reposition the right hand so that finger 2 is on the beat 4. In bar 12 take care to articulate the quarter notes in the left hand. In the right hand you will need to move finger 5 up on beat 4 to prepare for the following phrase.

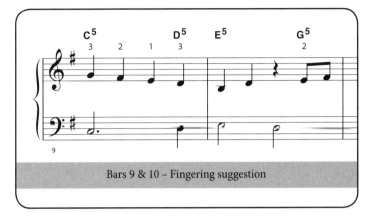

Bars 9 & 10 – Fingering suggestion

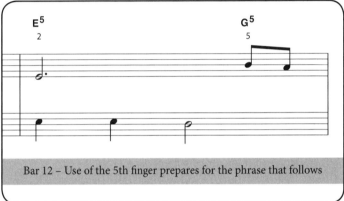

Bar 12 – Use of the 5th finger prepares for the phrase that follows

**Bars 13–16:**
This is pretty much a repeat of the previous four bars and the fingering will need the same attention. However, in bar 14 use the rest in the right hand to put your thumb on beat 4. This will put you in position to the end of the piece. In bars 15 & 16 the left hand has parallel chords (chords that move up in the same shape) and the same fingering should be used for all of them (1 & 5). Make sure that the last note is given its full value for a strong ending.

# Technical Exercises

In this section, the examiner will ask you to play a selection of exercises drawn from each of the three groups shown below. Groups A and B contain examples of the kinds of scales and chords you can use when playing the pieces. In Group C you will be asked to prepare the riff exercise and play it to the CD backing track. You do not need to memorise the exercises (and can use the book in the exam) but the examiner will be looking for the following: a prompt and accurate response, fluency and consistency of pulse.

Groups A and B are to be played at ♩ = 70. The examiner will give you this tempo in the exam. All scales and chords should be played using the piano patch.

## Group A: Scales ♩ = 70

All scales are to be prepared right hand only.

1. A minor pentatonic scale.

2. E minor pentatonic scale.

3. C major scale.

## Group B: Chords ♩=70

All chord sequences should be played with the right or left hand as directed by the examiner.

1. Chords i and iv in A minor.

2. Chords i and v in A minor.

3. Chords I and IV in C major.

4. Chords I and V in C major.

## Group C: Riff ♩=90

In the exam you will be asked to play the following riff to the backing track on the CD. The riff pattern shown in bar 1 should be played in the following bars using the nearest right hand inversions for the stated chords, referring to Group B above where necessary. The root notes of the chords to be played are shown in each bar.

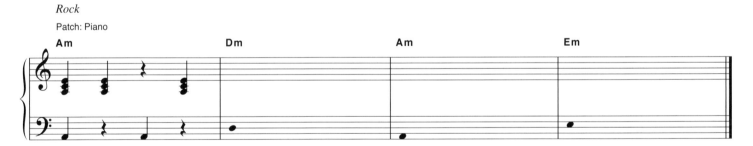

# Sight Reading

Printed below is the type of sight reading test you are likely to encounter in the exam. You will be asked to perform it using the piano patch on your keyboard. The sight reading test will be in the key of A minor pentatonic. The examiner will allow you 90 seconds to prepare it and will set the tempo for you on a metronome.

**Tempo** ♩=60

*Rock*

Patch: Piano

# Ear Tests

There are two ear tests in this grade. The examiner will play each test to you twice on CD. You will find one example of each type of test you will be given in the exam printed below.

## Test 1: Rhythm Recall

You will be asked to play back using the piano patch on your keyboard the given two bar rhythm on the note middle C on your keyboard. You will hear the rhythm played twice with a drum backing. There will then be a short break for you to practise the test and then the test will recommence and you will be required to play the rhythm to the drum backing. This test is continuous.

**Tempo** ♩=70

## Test 2: Melodic Recall

You will be asked to play back using the piano patch on your keyboard a simple melody of two bars composed from the first three notes of the C major scale. You will be given the tonic note and told the starting note and you will hear the test twice with a drum backing. There will then be a short break for you to practise the test and then the test will recommence and you will be required to play the melody with the drum backing. This test is continuous.

**Tempo** ♩=70

# General Musicianship Questions

You will be asked five General Musicianship Questions at the end of the exam. The examiner will ask questions based on pieces you have played in the exam. Some of the theoretical topics can be found in the Technical Exercises.

**Topics:**

i)      Music theory
ii)     Knowledge of your instrument

The music theory questions will cover the recognition of the following at this grade:

Note pitches
Note values
Time Signatures

Knowledge of parts of the keyboard:

Keys, on/off switch, volume control, patches
How black notes are grouped

Questions on all these topics will be based on pieces played by you in the exam. Tips on how to approach this part of the exam can be found in the Rockschool Companion Guide and on the Rockschool website: *www.rockschool.co.uk*.

# Entering Rockschool Exams

Entering a Rockschool exam is easy. Please read through these instructions carefully before filling in the exam entry form. Information on current exam fees can be obtained from Rockschool by ringing **0845 460 4747** or by logging on to our website *www.rockschool.co.uk*.

- You should enter for your exam when you feel ready.

- You can enter for any one of three examination periods. These are shown below with their closing dates.

| PERIOD | DURATION | CLOSING DATE |
|---|---|---|
| **Period A** | 1$^{st}$ February to 15$^{th}$ March | 1$^{st}$ December |
| **Period B** | 1$^{st}$ May to 31$^{st}$ July | 1$^{st}$ April |
| **Period C** | 23rd October to 15$^{th}$ December | 1$^{st}$ October |

**These dates will apply from 1st September 2006 until further notice**

- Please complete the form giving the information required. Please fill in the type and level of exam, the instrument, along with the period and year. Finally, fill in the fee box with the appropriate amount. You can obtain up to date information on all Rockschool exam fees from the website: *www.rockschool.co.uk*. You should send this form with a cheque or postal order (payable to Rockschool Ltd) to the address shown on the order form. **Please also indicate on the form whether or not you would like to receive notification via email.**

- Applications received after the expiry of the closing date may be accepted subject to the payment of an additional fee.

- When you enter an exam you will receive from Rockschool an acknowledgement letter or email containing a copy of our exam regulations.

- Rockschool will allocate your entry to a centre and you will receive notification of the exam, showing a date, location and time as well as advice of what to bring to the centre. We endeavour to give you four weeks' notice of your exam.

- You should inform Rockschool of any cancellations or alterations to the schedule as soon as you can as it is usually not possible to transfer entries from one centre, or one period, to another without the payment of an additional fee.

- Please bring your music book and CD to the exam. You may not use photocopied music, nor the music used by someone else in another exam. The examiner will sign each book during each examination. You may be barred from taking an exam if you use someone else's music.

- You should aim to arrive for your Debut exam fifteen minutes before the time stated on the schedule.

- Each Debut exam is scheduled to last for 15 minutes. You can use a small proportion of this time to tune up and get ready.

- Two to three weeks after the exam you will receive a copy of the examiner's mark sheet. Every successful player will receive a Rockschool certificate of achievement.